CW00868391

Sheila
the sheep

With Best Wishes.
Adrienne
2023

written and illustrated by

Adrienne Charles

Sheila the sheep had lived in the bush for six years
and loved living with all her friends, but now it was time to go home.
Her favourite time used to be out in the paddocks.

Sheila didn't like having her cosy wool shorn.

The sheep dogs, Tom, Paddy and Shep rounded up the mob for shearing.
They nipped at her heels and the dust hurt her eyes.

One year, at shearing time,
Sheila stayed behind,
so far back that not one of the dogs
saw that she was
missing!

Sheila wandered off into the bush, away from her mob.
On the way Sheila met new friends.
Maggie Magpie was very friendly
and enjoyed finding good things to eat
on Sheila's coat.

There was Horace the Echidna, who loved to snuffle and dig.

Native hens ran in all directions when they saw Sheila.

She couldn't catch them as they were so fast,

running in zigzags with their wings held high.

Pongo the Platypus would sometimes run

from the shallow creek then plunge

back into the cool water.

Wally Wombat was her favourite friend.

They both loved to graze the grass.

It was good to have his company, but Sheila still missed her mob.

Sheila wandered further and further away from the farm.

The farmers didn't know she was missing

... she was only one sheep in thousands.

The weather became very cold.

Winter was coming, so when Sheila's wool grew, she didn't mind.

It kept her warm on chilly nights.

When summer came her woolly coat protected her

from the hot sun so she was happy.

Each season her coat grew and grew
... and grew
... and grew
... and GREW!

Until ...

after all the years of living with her bush friends,
Sheila realised she was very, homesick and very, very tired.
All her friends were busy.

Horace snuffling for ants.
 Wally digging a better hole to live in,
  and Pongo was doing what a platypus loves to do ...
swimming and turning pebbles in the cool creek.

With her coat sooooooo heavy to carry around,
Sheila couldn't do anything at all.
Her daggy coat had collected twigs and bark
and was even a warm home for a mouse!
Sheila decided it was time to go home
where hopefully Tom, Paddy and Shep
would round her up with the rest of the mob.

But how could she get there?

Sheila's coat was so heavy her legs struggled to walk.
Every day she waited, her coat continued to grow ... and grow
... and grow!

Poor Sheila.

With her friends they set off
to find her way back to the farm.

Finally they came across a well-worn sheep track - could it take her home?
Round and round the track wound its way through the bush
until it got wider, and the bush became more open.
Sheila heard something she hadn't heard for a very long time ...
cars driving along the lonely bush road.

'Where am I?' thought Sheila.

Would this road lead her home?

Sheila staggered out of the bush.
Her long, shaggy, daggy, dirty, smelly, coat was just too heavy
and she slipped into a ditch on the side of the road!
Sheila was stuck! Sheila lay there.
All her bush friends tried to help
but they couldn't work out what to do.

'SCREE-ee, SCREE-ee, SCREE-ee!' The native hens called as they ran.

Surely someone would know something was wrong!

Sheila was worried when she saw Danny Devil. She knew how hungry devils could be.

He scuttled off to find easier prey when he heard the noisy hens.

Wally waddled by. He tried to dig her out but there were too many rocks.

Maggie Magpie chortled and danced around, trying to cheer her up.

All Sheila could do was wait.

Mr and Mrs Jones drove along the bush road and saw something very strange.

What was that sticking out of the ditch?

Was it an old bale of wool?

Farmer Jones looked closer.

Sheila didn't look very much alive ...

but suddenly she winked at Mr Jones!

Sheila was found!

Sheila was so happy, but even Mr and Mrs Jones
couldn't lift her on their own,
so they drove to the farm
to tell them about finding Sheila.

Sheila was so large she had to ride home in a trailer.

Instead of seeing her long lost mob,

there were reporters from everywhere waiting to make her famous.

This time Sheila didn't mind being shorn.
She was just so happy to be home.

She knew that from then on
she would stay with the mob
and be shorn EVERY YEAR!

• Launceston

T A S M A N I A

Buckland •

Hobart •

Tasmania is a beautiful heart-shaped island
found south of the Australian mainland.
Sheila lived at Twamley Farm in Buckland,
which is on the East Coast of Tasmania,
one hour's drive from Hobart.
The farm not only raises Merino sheep
for their very fine wool, but also has
cattle, and tree plantations.

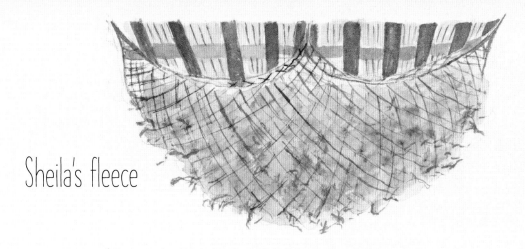

Sheila's fleece

Once a year the sheep are rounded up from the paddocks with the help of the kelpie sheep dogs and the musterers, then herded into pens for shearing.

Sheila is one of many lost sheep found laden with overgrown fleece. In 2004, Shrek was found in New Zealand carrying a record 27 kilograms of wool. Ten years later, Shaun the Sheep was found in the Tasmanian Midlands with a fleece weighing 23.5 kilograms. Then in 2015, Chris was found in bushland near Canberra carrying a hefty 40.5 kilograms.

Sheila was found on December 28, 2015, and she was shorn about a week later in early January 2016. Sheila's wool didn't quite break the Australian and New Zealand record, but certainly gave it a good nudge, weighing in at nearly 30 kilograms, breaking the Tasmanian record at that time. Sheila's story featured widely in the Australian media and caused a great deal of excitement in Tasmania.

The famous fleece still holds pride of place in the woolshed at Twamley Farm.

Woolshed glossary

Thanks to Lona Turvey of Twamley Farm and Cameron, an experienced shearer who supplied some of this information.

BALE The fleece is compressed into a large bale determined by weight, using a large machine called a wool press. The maximum weight is 204 kilograms.

'BLACK WOOL' Shearers call this out if there is black discolouration in the fleece. It is not worth as much.

BLADES Old-fashioned shears for hand shearing.

BLOW A single sweeping cut of fleece.

BRANDING The brand of the property applied to the sheep.

COBBLER A rough sheep. There are 'rough' sheep and 'easy' sheep and the shearers usually grab the 'easy' sheep first.

CRUTCHING The removal of wool from the sheep's rear end and around head and ears to prevent fly strike. (This is done at a different time to shearing).

DAGS Manure caught around the sheep's rear end. If very bad a shearer could earn more money.

DUNGAREES Trousers worn by shearers.

GUN/TOP GUN The fastest shearer in the shed.

JACKY HOWE Singlet worn by shearers.

JUMBUCK Sheep.

LET GO PEN After the sheep have been shorn, they are let go into a pen for counting and branding at the end of each shearing run.

LONG BLOW A sweep from tail to the head.

MICRONS The thickness of the wool fibre which determines the quality of the fleece.

MOB A large (or small) number of sheep together.

MOCCASINS Footwear worn by the shearer. Usually made from leather, or nylon felt for comfort.

MUSTERING/GATHERING The rounding up of the sheep from different paddocks or bush runs in readiness for shearing.

PENNING UP Placing sheep in catching pens for shearing.